TWO DOZEN IN TWO PARTS

Arrangements for Choir or Ensemble

BY

TOM FETTKE · CAMP KIRKLAND · DENNIS ALLEN
JOSEPH LINN · DOUG HOLCK · MOSIE LISTER · MARTY PARKS
RUSSELL MAULDIN · DENNIS CRISER · RANDY SMITH

Two-part Arrangements by Tom Fettke

KANSAS CITY, MO 64141

CONTENTS

4

Magnify Him

RANDY VADER and K. T.

KIRK TALLEY
Arr. by Mosie Lister
2-part edition by Tom Fettke

8

In Christ Alone

S. C. and D. K.

SHAWN CRAIG and DON KOCH
Arr. by Dennis Allen
2-part edition by Tom Fettke

10

*A male singing the upper part and a female singing the lower part is preferable.
In 2-part choir configuration, men should be on the upper part.

14

Rejoice in His Love

includes

My Savior's Love
Such Love

Arr. by Tom Fettke

*Such Love (C. Bishop-Robert Harkness)

CD: 11

Touch Your People Once Again

P. K.

PELLE KARLSSON
Arr. by Tom Fettke

24

We Sing the Mighty Power of God
and Hosanna, Loud Hosanna

Vs. 1: ISAAC WATTS
Vs. 2: JENNETTE THRELFALL

Gesangbuch, 1784
Arr. by Doug Holck and Tom Fettke

28

No More Night

W. H.

WALT HARRAH
Arr. by Tom Fettke

With joyful anticipation ♩ = ca. 84

30

*or choir parts as in the 1st verse.

34

No more tears, nev-er cry-ing a-gain.

Prais - es to the great "I Am,"
All prais - es to the great "I Am," We will

live in the light of the ris - en

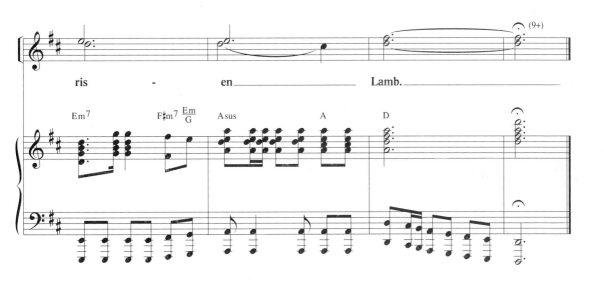

It's Different Now

D. B.

DAVID BEATTY
Arr. by Mosie Lister
2-part edition by Tom Fettke

38

40

I Want to Be Like Jesus

with

Lord, Be Glorified

Arr. by Tom Fettke

**Measures 7 through 10 may be more effective singing unison melody.

*"I Want to Be Like Jesus" (Thomas Chisholm-David Ives)

28 A little slower ♩ = ca. 86 *mp*

His like-ness shin - ing forth in me. I want to be like

A little slower

mp

32 **CD: 27**

Je - sus.

mf

35 Faster ♩ = ca. 90

Part I *mf*

Part II

O per-fect life of Christ,_____ my Lord!

Faster

mf smoothly

39

I want to be like Je - sus._____ My rec - om-pense and

my re- ward, That I may be like Je - sus.

His Spir - it fill___ my hun - g'ring soul, His pow - er all___ my

life con - trol; My deep - est prayer, my high - est goal—

That I may be like Je - sus.

Peace in the Midst of the Storm

S. R. A.

STEPHEN R. ADAMS
Arr. by Russell Mauldin
2-part edition by Tom Fettke

48

Easter Call to Worship

CHARLES WESLEY and T. F.

JOHN DARWALL and TOM FETTKE

Now and Forevermore

M. P.

MARTY PARKS
2-part edition by Tom Fettke

58

Wor - thy, Wor - thy, King of kings and Lord of lords! Wor - thy is the Lamb of God,_____

Now and for - ev - er - more! The earth breaks its si - lence, in glo - ry pro-claims: "He is not here, He is

"Christ, the Lord, Is Risen Today"
(Charles Wesley - Lyra Davidica)

All cre - a - tion sings,_____ All cre - a - tion

sings:_____ Christ, the

Lord, is ris - en to - day!_____

Al -

CD: 35

- le - lu - ia, Al - le - lu, Al - le -

(cued notes optional) Div.

lu - ia! _____ Wor - thy,

Wor - thy, King of kings and Lord of lords!

Wor - thy is the Lamb of God, _____

My Jesus, I Love Thee

WILLIAM R. FEATHERSTON

DEBORAH CRISER
Arr. by Dennis Criser
2-part edition by Tom Fettke

66

CD: 38
mf
In man-sions of
decresc.
mf
44
glo - ry and end-less de - light,
8va
48
I'll ev-er a - dore Thee in heav - en so
bright.
52
cresc.
I'll sing with the glit - ter - ing
cresc.
8va

68

Be Still, My Soul

KATHERINE VON SCHLEGEL, tr. by Jane Borthwick
New lyrics and lyric adaptations by NAN ALLEN

"Finlandia" by JEAN SIBELIUS
Arr. by Dennis Allen
2-part edition by Tom Fettke

General text: Be still, my soul; the Lord is on thy side,_____
Christmas text: Be still, my soul; the Lord is on our side,_____

Bear pa - tient - ly the cross of grief and pain.
To guide and com - fort through our grief and pain.

70

CD: 40

Be still, my soul; the hour is has - t'ning
O praise the Lord, O praise the King of

Broader

on___ When we shall be for -
heav - en. The Prince of Peace has

I Will Rejoice

M. W. S. and B. D.

MICHAEL W. SMITH and BEVERLY DARNALL
Arr. by Tom Fettke

Part I: He is the Cap-tain of a heav-en-ly ar - my. Praise Him, — oh, — praise — Him!

My De-fend - er, no foe can harm me. Praise Him, — oh, — praise — Him!

78

'* if range is too high.'

noise,_____ a joy-ful noise._____ I will___ re-joice

noise,_____ a joy-ful noise. I will___ re-joice_____

Part I

Part II 'til the moun - tains and the val - leys ring. I will___ re-joice_____

'til the depths_ of my soul can sing. God reigns,___ let the earth pro - claim.

80

His Name Is Wonderful
with
My Wonderful Lord

Tenderly ♩ = ca. 69

Arr. by Tom Fettke

82

*"His Name Is Wonderful" (Audrey Mieir)

bow at Thy shrine, my **Sav** - ior di - vine, My **won** - der-ful, won - der-ful **Lord.**

His name___ is Won - der - ful, His name___ is

CD: 46

Part I
Unison

Part II

Won - der-ful, His name___ is Won- der- ful–

Je - sus, my Lord. He is___ the

Might - y King, Mas - ter___ of ev - 'ry-thing,

CD: 47

His name___ is Won - der-ful– Je - sus, my

Bow down_____ be - fore Him,

Love and_____ a - dore Him, His name_____ is

Won - der - ful– Je - sus, my Lord,

Je - sus, my Lord, Je - sus, my

Come, Believe in His Name

B. A.

BOB ASHTON
Arr. by Camp Kirkland
and Tom Fettke

Come, be - lieve____ in His name,_____ be-

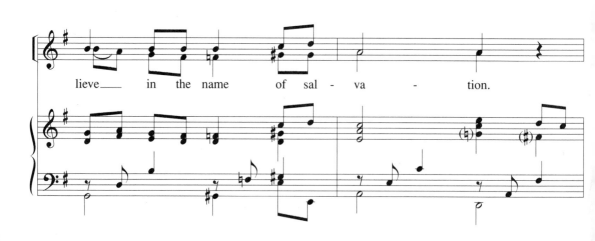

lieve____ in the name of sal - va - tion.

Great Grace Medley

includes

All Because of God's Amazing Grace
All in the Name of Jesus

Arr. by Joseph Linn
2-part edition by Tom Fettke

CD: 50   With thanks ♩ = ca. 80

6 *"All Because of God's Amazing Grace" (Stephen R. Adams)

Part I

Part II mel.

A - maz - ing grace! Oh, how sweet___ the sound that

saved___ a poor sin-ner like me.___ Tho'

once I was lost, yet now I am found; Tho' I was

91

cause of God's a - maz - ing grace!

*"All in the Name of Jesus" (Stephen R. Adams)

1. Truth_____ and beau-ty_____ and hap - pi - ness– It's

2. Care_____ and com-fort,_____ heal - ing and grace– It's

all_____ in the name_____ of Je - sus.

all_____ in the name_____ of Je - sus._____

58 All

Life ev - er - last - ing and free,____

fill - ment____ and bless - ing un - told,____

62 Part I mel. *mf* Div.

Part II

All that I've longed for and all____ I need– It's

mel. *f*

Hope for to - mor - row and help for to - day– It's

mf-f

| CD: 52 | *1st time* |
| CD: 54 | *2nd time* |

66

all____ in the name____ of Je - sus.____

all____ in the name____ of Je - sus.____

mp

Je - sus, Je - sus– He's here and He will show you the way. Oh,_____ Je - sus, Je - sus– He's all that you

CD: 53

1

need _____ to - day. _____

2

88

day. _____ Je -

(')

sus, Je - sus,

92 rit.

mf

3

3

All _____ in the name of Je - sus. _____

mf

rit.

(8)

Traveling On

includes

I Feel Like Traveling On
We'll Work Till Jesus Comes

Arr. by Tom Fettke
and Randy Smith

*"I Feel Like Traveling On" (William Hunter-Anonymous)

98

100

*"We'll Work Till Jesus Comes" (Elizabeth Mills-William Miller)
1st time: Part II (or men) only
2nd time: All
cues notes opt. (if ladies are singing this line)

When I Look Into Your Holiness

W. P., C. P.

WAYNE and CATHY PERRIN
Arr. by Tom Fettke

107

He Is Here

K. T.

KIRK TALLEY
Arr. by Tom Fettke

23 *Solo (or choir unison)*

I sense an awe-some mov-ing of the Ho-ly Spir-it.

27

I see His coun-te-nance rest-ing on your face.

31 *Solo (or men)* mel.

Ladies

I know that there are an-gels hov-'ring all a-round us,____ For the

35 **CD: 64** cresc. *Part I* *mf*

Part II

pres-ence of the Lord is in this place. He is

cresc.

For God So Loved

Adapted from Scripture by S. D.

STUART DAUERMANN
Arr. by Tom Fettke

116

*Option: duet may be sung by the choir– men sing high part, ladies sing low part.

118

122

Where No One Stands Alone

M. L.

MOSIE LISTER
Arr. by Keith Phillips
2-part edition by Tom Fettke

CD: 72

124

dark - ness as black as could be;_____ And my

heart felt a - lone, and I cried, "O Lord, don't

hide Your face___ from me."_____ Hold my

hand all the way, ev-'ry hour,___ ev-'ry day, From

here   to the great_____ un - known._____

Take   my__ hand,   let   me__ stand_____ Where

no one_____   stands   a - lone._____

CD: 73   rit.   mf

mel.

Like a

decresc.   rit.   mf

king, I may live____ in a pal - ace so tall____ With great rich - es to

call____ my own;_____ But I don't____ know a thing____ in the

whole wide world That's worse than be - ing a - lone.____

Hold my hand all the way, ev - 'ry hour,____ ev - 'ry day, From

here to the great___ un - known.___ Take my___

hand, let me__ stand__ Where no one___ stands a -

lone.___ lone.___ Where no one,___

__ Where no one___ stands a - lone.___

The God of Hope Be with You

(a cappella)

KEN BIBLE
Inspired by Romans 15:33

TOM FETTKE

In Majesty He Will Come

D. T. and M. T.

DICK and MELODIE TUNNEY
Arr. by Joseph Linn
2-part edition by Tom Fettke

Born_____ of a might - y God,

sent from His heav'n - ly____ throne,

Giv - en to reign o - ver

kings and priests, the sins of man to a - tone,

The Mes- si - ah will re - turn, the hour___ un- known___ to

man. A fan- fare of praise will in- hab - it___ the earth as cre-

a - tion___ re- joic - es in Him!___

132

134

earth will bow____ to this most ho - ly____ One. In____

maj - es - ty He will come.____

____ In maj - es - ty, in maj - es - ty He will

come.____

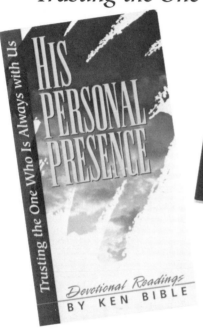